Text and illustration ©Anahita Teymorian

This edition published in 2017 by Tiny Owl Publishing Ltd, London

Written and illustrated by Anahita Teymorian

Translated by Azita Rassi

Graphic designer: Elahe Javanmanrd

ISBN 978-1-910328-23-1

A CIP catalogue record of this book is available from the British Library

A Bird Like Himself

Anahita Teymorian

One day
something pale and
oval was left all on its own
and with nobody to look after
it. The oval thing was warm, and it
rocked a little back and forth before
suddenly …

.... CRACK!

Out of the egg came a fat little chick.

The animals living round about didn't know how to care for a baby bird. But there was nobody else to look after the chick, so the animals did their best.

They tried this . . .

...and this.

The animals didn't always get it right, but they did love that fat little chick.

They called him Baby, because he was everyone's baby.

The animals gave Baby whatever he wanted.
"I'm hungry!" said Baby.

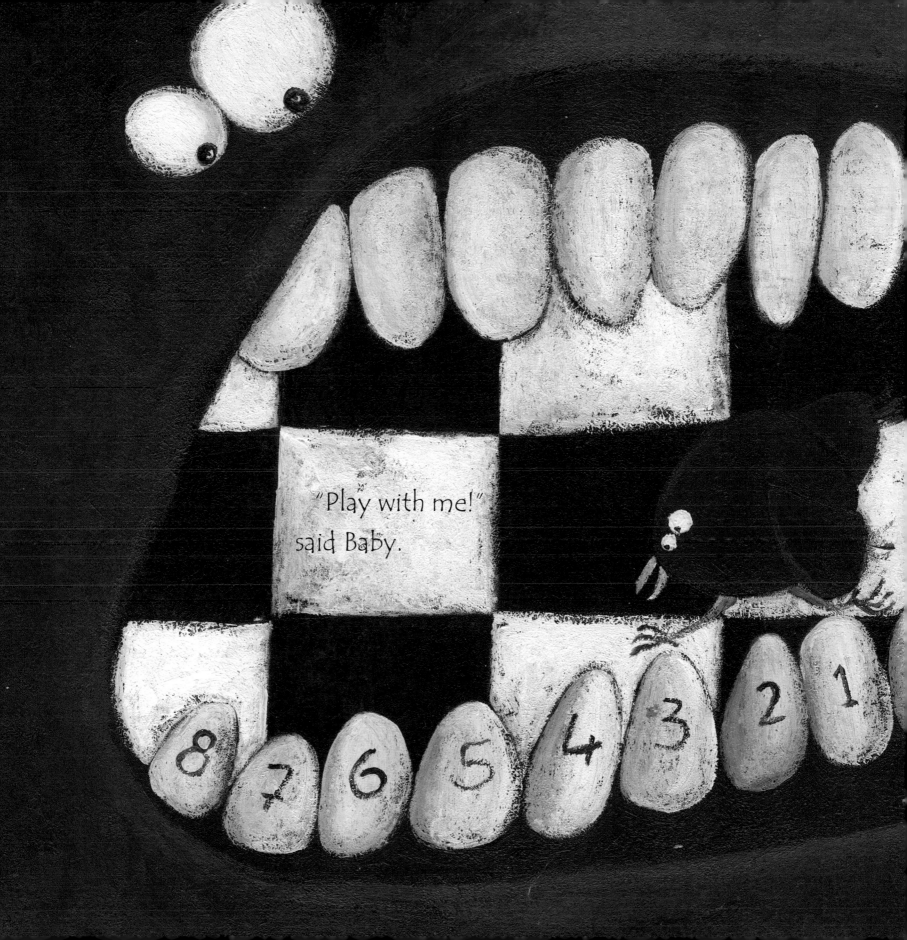

Baby grew **bigger,**
but did he grow wiser?

Baa....

Sometimes Baby went,
"Baa baa!"

Sometimes he went, "Moo moo!"

moooo

But there was one thing that Baby didn't learn
how to do.
"You must learn to fly," said the animals.
"What's 'fly'?" said Baby.
"Oh dear," said the animals.

The animals tried to teach Baby how to fly, but of course they couldn't show him how to do it.

Baby tried and tried, but he could NOT *fly.*

Winter was coming. A bird like Baby should fly
south to keep warm when the weather gets cold.
Whatever would happen to a bird who couldn't fly?

Then Baby saw a bird who was – Just like him!
"Will you be my friend?" he asked.

But the bird flapped her wings and began to fly away.
So guess what Baby did?

Without even thinking about it, Baby flapped his
own wings, and then HE was flying too.

And away they both happily flew,
towards the winter sun.

About the book

This is a funny, but profound, story about parental love
and growing up.

Anahita Teymorian

Author/illustrator Anahita Teymorian also works with animation in her native Iran. Her books are known all over the world, and her work has been featured in major international exhibitions. She has won awards at Bologna Children's Book Fair, Noma Concours, and Octagonal in France.